TO
FIND
JESUS

TO
FIND
JESUS

written by
Edward C. Peterson
and Barbara Nan Peterson

with illustrations by Jim Padgett

ABINGDON PRESS

NASHVILLE   NEW YORK

Authors' Statement

This "might-have-been" story is based on
the Bible, but woven around many imagina-
tive scenes, settings, and conversations. The
result is a connected story of Jesus' life
which goes beyond the strict Bible account
to imagine Jesus' relationships with his disciples, his deeds, and the real life situations
out of which his teachings may have arisen.

Bible ideas have been protected while words
have been paraphrased and simplified to
make them understandable to the young.
Events have been invented, emotions in-
terpreted, and disciples dressed in personali-
ties where the Bible has not reported de-
tail. Extra-biblical traditions have helped
provide background, and the work of bibli-
cal scholars has been influential. The effort
has been to bring to the twentieth-century
child an understandable story, true to the
Bible spirit and record, but told in such a
way that the old story seems newly relevant
for today's need.

As the four New Testament Gospels are interpretations of the life of Jesus, so To Find Jesus is a witness of faith in him. It is not desirable that this fictionalized account of our Lord's life should take the place of the Bible record. It is to be hoped that the actual Bible text will be more meaningful because of the reading of this story.

The first four biographers of Jesus prepared their separate accounts to speak to their own first-century world. This story seeks to witness to the same truth as did the Gospel writers—that God was in Jesus Christ, and to find Jesus is to find God.

Contents

TO
FIND
JESUS

The Three Tall Men

High over the resting caravan
the dark sky was dotted
with bright stars.
The stars twinkled brighter
as the campfire flickered lower,
burning down—burning out.
The heavenly lights looked cool
in the dark hot night.
Against the black, black sky
the bright stars sparkled and glittered.
There was no moon that night.
But there were stars and stars
and more stars.
The servants in the caravan
whispered about the stars.
Especially about the one
brighter than all the rest.
The servants lay down
on their sleeping mats on the hard ground.
They looked up into the star-filled sky.
They wondered about the little child
they had seen.
With a last look at the special star,
one by one
they all fell asleep.
All but the three tall men.

The three tall men who did not sleep
wore splendid robes.

The three tall men who did not sleep
were in charge of the donkeys, the camels,
and the servants.
These three tall men owned the heavy loads
that had been lifted from the backs
of the animals so they could rest
in the dark hot night.
The three tall men stood gazing at
the brightest of the stars.
The most important star—
of all the many, many stars
in the dark, dark sky—
was the star followed by the three
tall men and all their servants
and donkeys and camels, with their costly,
heavy loads.

That star had led this caravan
from the distant country in the East
to worship the newborn baby king.
They had gone to the palace to find
the baby.
But King Herod had not been pleased.
"I am King of Jerusalem," he had said.
"I am King of this whole land.
No baby has been born in my palace.
No one is going to be King of Jerusalem
and of this land but Herod."
King Herod's words were firm.
But King Herod had seen the bright star too
and he knew men were hoping,
were looking for another king . . .
a king to be greater than Herod,
a king worthy of the brightest of stars.

These three tall men had come from afar—
searching for a King of the Jews
that all other kings could worship.
"We seek the King of kings,"
the three tall men had said. The men,
who were themselves three rich kings
of the East,
remembered King Herod's words:
"Find him. Find your newborn king.
Come and tell me where you find him.
I, too, will worship him."

"We did right not to return
to the palace," said the first tall man.
"Herod really wants to harm the child.
We did right to protect the little king.
God will use this child to lead his people."

13

The other two tall men nodded their heads.
"You are right. You are right," they said.
"We did right not to return to tell Herod
that we found the child."
"I will never forget that child," said the
second tall man.
"What an important child!
What an important man that child will be.
God is in him, leading men to truth.
I remember that his eyes shone brighter
than the shining gold
I left as a kingly gift for him."
"I will always remember,"
said the first tall man,
"his mother's smile, Mary's smile of joy.
How brightly glowed her face
as I placed my costly gift of frankincense
at the little king's feet
and worshiped God's young king."
"And I shall not forget, but long remember—
Joseph's strong, firm clasp,"
said the last tall man.
"It was strong, as the hand of a man
must be strong to guard and protect
a child sent by God.
Joseph's hand was as firm and hard
as the precious gift of myrrh
I gave to the child."

"Glory to God!"
the three tall men chanted together.
"Glory to God in the highest!
Thanks be for the child
who has come from God—

"The child whose name is Jesus!
And thanks be for Mary and Joseph,
who will protect and teach the child.
Grant that Jesus
may lead all men to God—
even as the young king's bright star
led us to worship him."

The tallest man, still praying,
laid himself on his costly kingly rug,
ready for rest.
The next tallest man
reclined on his mat on the hard, hard ground
in the dark, dark night, thanking God.
The last tall man was filled with joy.
He was homeward bound.
He had worshiped the King of kings.
The way home would be long.
It would be far for the donkeys,
far for the camels, far for the servants,
and far for the three tall Wise Men,
who had traveled from afar . . .
to find Jesus.

The Lost Boy

"I will see him if he passes here,"
she thought.
She was trying hard not to cry.
She looked far ahead toward Nazareth.
She squinted her eyes back toward
Jerusalem.
"My son is lost," she said in an anxious
voice.
"My son is lost."

Mary, Joseph, and young Jesus
had been to the great city.
Many travelers had gone to Jerusalem
for the feast of the Passover.
They had prayed in the beautiful Temple.
They had given their gifts and
left their offerings to God there.
They had been taught by the great teachers.
They had been blessed by the priests.
Now the people were all going home.
Mary and Joseph had started for home too.
It was then that they realized it.
Jesus was not with them.
He must be lost!

Mary looked into each familiar passing face.
"Have you seen him?
Have you seen my son?" she asked.
"Not today. Not today," they all answered.

"Is Jesus with you, John?
Is Jesus with you?" Mary called.
John, like Jesus, was twelve years old.
"I have not seen him," he said.
"I have not seen him today."

The dust seemed dustier.
The passing crowds seemed noisier.
The heat seemed hotter.
And the night was coming fast.

Mary's throat was dry.
She wiped a tear slipping down her cheek.
John tried to comfort her.
"Jesus may be helping blind Samuel.
Perhaps he is carrying little lame Saul
and his crutches.
Perhaps he is with Rabbi Ben Eli,
talking about God.
He could be ahead with our friends,
telling of his adventures in Jerusalem."
"Thank you, John," Mary smiled.
"And God grant you a safe journey."
And to herself, she added,
"And the Lord God watch over my lost boy."

Mary and Joseph said:
"We must return to Jerusalem at once.
We must search for Jesus there."
They traveled through the dark night.

Mary prayed. Joseph prayed.
They walked until they reached Jerusalem.
They were ever so tired by morning.

18

But they were too worried to rest.
They searched up and down the streets.
They asked about Jesus in the shops,
in the marketplace.
They looked for him at every friend's home.
They asked the soldiers passing by:
"Have you seen a lost boy?"
They searched for him the whole day long.
They searched for him a second whole day.
They searched for him a third whole day.

"Joseph," said Mary at last,
"let us go to the Temple again.
Let us go to the House of God
to pray once again for Jesus' safety."
As they climbed the stairs
to the great Temple court,
Joseph held Mary's hand to comfort her.
They were both tired with worry.
Just then, they passed a circle
of listening teachers.
A voice spoke clearly from the
center of the circle.
"God's Law is the law of love,"
the clear voice said.
"God's way is the way of truth."
The teachers answered: "Well said. Well
said."
"Joseph!" Mary gasped, grabbing his arm.
"That voice! It's Jesus! It's our Jesus!"
They were too surprised to move.
"He's a thinker, an amazing boy!"
Joseph heard a teacher say.
"He is not content with simple questions."
"He has deep thoughts," a priest said.
"He will surely be a great teacher
for God when he grows up," another said.

Mary and Joseph pressed into the group.
Jesus saw them and smiled.
"I must go now," he said to the teachers.
"Thank you for talking of God with me."
"Thank you, Jesus," the teachers answered.
"Mary and Joseph are blessed of God
to have raised so fine a boy."

20

The teachers went away.
Young Jesus stood looking up.
He looked up into Mary's tired face.
He looked up into Joseph's frowning face.
Mary and Joseph wanted to speak.
They were not sure what they should say.
Joseph turned to Mary. "My wife," he said,
"let us remember that our prayers
have been answered.

"Let us remember to thank God for his help."
Then Joseph turned to young Jesus.
"Where have you been?
Where have you been?
We have been searching, looking, hunting
everywhere for you.
We have been searching for three long days."
Mary said: "My son! My son!
Why have you treated us so?
We thought you were lost.
We have searched everywhere for you.
We have feared for your safety."
Jesus seemed surprised.
He had not meant to worry his family.
He did not mean to trouble them.
"Why have you been searching, searching,
searching everywhere?" he asked.
"I have been here, right here.
I have not been lost.
Have you not taught me always
to be about the Lord God's work?
Did you not know that I was sure to be
in God's House?"
Joseph and Mary pondered the words
in their hearts.
"Thanks be to thee, O God," they prayed,
"for a child who loves thee
and thy House."
But they did not understand Jesus' words.
Joseph did not understand.
Mary did not understand.
But they did know they had found
their lost boy.

The Time for Going

"Jesus," said Joseph one day,
"you are a fine carpenter.
I am very proud
of the strong benches
and beautiful tables you make."
"Thank you, sir," answered Jesus.
"All I know of shaping wood
into useful items
I have learned from you."
Joseph smiled. "I could not ask
for a better boy," he said.
"Now," Joseph continued,
"it is time for us to speak together
about your life work.
It is time to speak of carpentry.
The law of our people says:
'A son shall take up his father's work.'
One day my carpenter's shop will be yours."
Jesus squared his shoulders.
He stood taller than Joseph.
His back was straight.
His arms were strong.
He was no longer a child.
He had become a man.
"Sir," Jesus began,
"you know of my great love for you.
You know of my great love for my family.
You know, too, that I have always tried
to help you in your work."

He brushed some sawdust from his bench.
"You have always taught me
that the service of God
is the most important work.
I must serve God!"
Joseph did not look surprised.
"Has God put it in your heart
to take up a special work?" he asked.
Jesus answered in a firm voice.
"I know the work of God
must be my own work.
I know the love of God must lead me.
God must have all of me."
"Your words make me proud and sad,"
Joseph said.
"What will you do? What will you be?
Where will you go?"
"God has not yet made all clear to me,"
Jesus explained.
"But this much I know.
My life work is not to be in your shop.
I must be busy in doing what God wants.
I must go wherever God leads me.
My life cannot be spent in your home.
I will not live in comfort or safety.
I may even live in daring and danger
for God.
My work is not in the shaping of wood.
My life must be spent
in seeking and saving people
who have turned away from God;
who have become lost to God.
I must tell all that God is our Father."
"Jesus! Jesus!" Joseph said.

24

"From the day of your birth,
and even before,
I have known God was sending you
into the world for a special work.
I have known you to be God's chosen Son
from the very beginning.
When it is time for you to leave,
you will go with my blessing."
Joseph went on:
"I remember well
when you were but a small baby,
and we took you up to the
holy Temple.
The priest named Simeon told us then
that God had a mighty plan for you."
Joseph laid his big hands
on Jesus' broad shoulders
and blessed him.

The days passed.
Joseph and Jesus worked side by side
in the Nazareth carpenter shop.
One day, Jesus said to Joseph:
"Sir, the time has come.
The time of my going has come."
Joseph nodded and laid down his tools.
"Where will you go?" he asked.
"I must go to talk with John,"
Jesus answered.
"Then I will go into the wilderness
to think, to pray, and to be alone.
I must wait before God.
God will make clear to me
what I must do next."

"Jesus," Joseph said, "John
already has gone to the wilderness.
He has become a great preacher.
Will you preach too?
John is baptizing the people.
Will you baptize the people too?"
"I cannot say yet," Jesus explained.
"I am not sure.
God will make it clear to me.
When I go to John the Baptizer,
I may ask him to lower me into the
wetness of the water of the river Jordan.
In the water I could pray that God
would take away everything that keeps me
from being his perfect Son."
"When do you leave, Jesus?
When do you leave?"
"In the morning, I leave.
In the morning," said Jesus,
"I will be ready then to put myself
under the highest law,
under the greatest love,
into the strongest protection.
In the morning
I will leave all
to follow God."

"Go," said Joseph,
"and when you go,
be strong and be of good courage.
Your name is Jesus
because you have been sent by God
to call his people away from all
that separates them from God.

"God be praised!
Now the Lord God take you.
In him you shall ever go in peace.
Now leave me
and be known to all as God's own Son."
Jesus put down his tools.
He laid aside his carpenter's apron.
Jesus kissed Joseph.
Joseph's hug was as firm as his love.
In the morning,
after his good-byes, after some tears,
Jesus left his Nazareth home.
He left his much-loved family.
He left the little carpenter shop.
He did not look back.
The time to go had come.
He belonged to God.

Toward the Jordan

Jesus was feeling glad and sad.
He was leaving home.
He was sad to be leaving Nazareth.
For years, it had been his home.
He knew all of its streets
and each of its buildings.
He knew all of its people.
He even knew each of the pets of Nazareth.
He was sad to be leaving the carpenter shop.
He knew every corner and every tool.
He was sad to be leaving the house
that had been so long his home.
Most of all, he was sad to be leaving
Mary and Joseph.
It was not easy for the young man, Jesus,
to leave the place he knew the best,
and the people he loved the most.
This is why Jesus was feeling sad.

But Jesus was feeling glad, too.
"God has a new life he wants me to follow,"
Jesus remembered.
"It is sad to leave what I know and love,
to walk into what I do not know.
But with God to lead me, with God to keep
me safe, and with God to help me be brave,
it will be exciting to walk new roads,
to see new faces, to take up a new work,
and to rest in different places."

He was excited about the call of God
to serve God's people.
God had a great work for him to do.
But what was it? Everything was not clear.
As Jesus imagined all that would be new,
that might await him down the road,
his heart was glad.
As he followed the curve of the road,
Jesus kicked a pebble out of his way.
His thoughts were very serious now.
Often Jesus had worried about the
many poor people everywhere
with no one to help them find work.
Would God use him to help the poor?
It troubled Jesus deeply
to watch hungry people go without food,
while those with plenty of food
they could share seemed not to care.
Would God use him to feed the hungry?
And ever since Jesus was little,
his heart had been touched
by the sight of blind people, lame people,
and sick people.
Frequently, Jesus had prayed that one day
God would give him the gift of healing
so that he would have power
to make deaf people hear again,
those without sight, to see,
those crippled, to walk,
and the sick to be returned to health.
"Perhaps God will use me to heal the sick,"
Jesus thought.
Then, too, Jesus worried often about
all the people who had no one to teach them.

30

"Without a teacher, how can people learn
what is right?" Jesus said out loud.
"Perhaps God will use me
to teach those who have no teacher."

31

Jesus walked faster now.
His thoughts were racing faster
than his feet.
"Perhaps God is calling me
to lead my country to freedom."
This idea came because just then
Jesus saw coming toward him
a company of Roman soldiers.
They were marching in step
as the captain shouted orders to them.
Jesus remembered how often
he had seen such soldiers before.
He remembered seeing soldiers
hurt the citizens of Nazareth.
Sometimes the soldiers were very cruel.
Sometimes they used their swords to force
the people to obey their orders.
Some of the soldiers stole from the people.
Some of the soldiers took whatever they
wanted from the people.
The people were angry and afraid.
The people could not fight back,
because the land where Jesus lived
had no army of its own.
The army belonged to Rome.
It controlled all the people of Judea.
Often Jesus had heard the men of Nazareth
speak with hate about the powerful Roman
army that occupied their small country.
"Someday," they said, "God will deliver us
from this army that has conquered our land.
Someday, God will raise up a leader
who will deliver us from our enemies.
Someday, Rome's army must be driven out."

32

"O God, send us a great leader,
like mighty King David of long ago,
to save us from the rule of the Roman army,"
the men of Nazareth would pray.
Just then, the soldiers passed by Jesus.
Jesus looked back over his shoulder
to watch them march
so proud and so sure
toward the town of Nazareth
from which he had just come.
"Perhaps God will use me
to drive out the Roman army,"
Jesus thought.

But it was hard to think of himself
as a man of war and as one who would
lead an army of hating Jewish soldiers
into war against the Roman soldiers.
Jesus could not even find it in his heart
to hate the young men who had just
passed by him on the Nazareth road.
"They have their own problems,"
Jesus thought.
"They are far from their home and country.
They do not look as if they want to be here.
I wonder if they know that
God is the great King of all countries
and that he is to be known in love, not war?"

Jesus took out the bread he was carrying.
"Thanks be to thee, O Lord,
who giveth bread," Jesus prayed.
Jesus broke off a piece of the bread
and started to eat as he walked.

He was not so busy with his thoughts
that he forgot to take time
to enjoy the sights of the countryside.
"What a beautiful day," Jesus sang
as he started up another hill,
following the winding road.
"God has made everything beautiful
in its time!"
His step moved into a lively rhythm.
"Now I must watch for the road that
will take me toward the river Jordan."
With this thought, Jesus turned
his thinking toward his cousin, John.

John the Baptizer was said to be, even then,
preaching and teaching the way of God.
He was, the travelers had told Jesus,
baptizing many in the Jordan River.
Great crowds were going to hear him preach.
Even the citizens of Jerusalem
were leaving the city to hear his sermons
preached by the riverside in the country.
Many called John one of the great prophets
of the past come to life again.
"John the Baptist speaks out for God,"
the people said.
"It will be good to see John again,"
Jesus nodded.
Jesus was going to join the crowds.
Jesus was going to see his cousin again.
Jesus was eager to hear John's new message
from God that the people came to hear.
"John is telling
how God will save my people,"
Jesus remembered.
"Perhaps through John,
God will make known
to me the nature of my special work."
With this thought in mind
Jesus came to the crossroads.
"It is clear to me now," Jesus said.
"God will speak to me through John.
God will speak."
Jesus gave one look back toward Nazareth,
the town of his childhood and youth,
his family and friends.
Then Jesus turned down the road that led
toward the Jordan River and his new life.

The Journey

"Have you heard of John the Baptizer?"
Jesus smiled a greeting
to one of the merchants
resting in the shade by the side of the road.
The merchant and his caravan
were making camp to spend the night.
The merchant looked up at the stranger.
"Who has not heard of him?"
the merchant answered.
"He is being talked of everywhere."
Jesus threw his pack to the ground
and sat down in response to the inviting
gesture of the merchant.
"I would like to hear him,"
the merchant said.
"But my friends who have heard him say
his words burn like fire
into the minds of his hearers.
They say one should not go to hear John
unless he wants his conscience hurt."
"I want to hear him, too," Jesus replied.
"What good is a conscience
if it is not working?"
They both laughed.
"Do you know where John is now?"
Jesus asked.
"Do you know where I can find him?"
"Well, not exactly," the merchant said.
"I know he is usually found

in the countryside by the river.
Are you on your way to hear him, then?"
the merchant asked.
"More than to hear him," said Jesus.

"John was my boyhood friend.
He is my cousin by birth, and I
plan to spend some time with him.
Of course, I will hope to hear him preach."
"Then you should prepare
to hear a voice like thunder, they say.
Some say that when he preaches
you forget his booming voice,
for what he says lets you think only of God.
Some have called John
'the Thunder Preacher'
because his ideas are so big
and his voice is so loud."
Jesus nodded in understanding.
"He was strong as a boy.
As a man of God,
his strength would be greater."
The merchant stood up.
"Stranger," he smiled,
"we have much we can talk about.
Will you not stay to share our evening food?
Will you not sleep in our camp with us?
There are among my companions
those who have heard the great preacher.
Last year, on one of our journeys,
one of my caravan members stayed behind
to become one of John's followers.
There will be much for us to talk about.
Do stay with us."
"I will gladly visit and accept your kindness,"
said Jesus. "And I thank you.
Here, let me help you unload the camels."
As Jesus shared in the caravan's labor,
he was introduced to the other merchants,

each by name. They were all surprised
to learn that a cousin
of the famous Jordan prophet
was to be their special guest.

In the morning, upon leaving the caravan,
Jesus continued his walking.
It was a long way to that part of the Jordan
where John was last reported to be.
Some of the caravan said they had heard him
preaching as far north as where
the Lake of Galilee empties its water
into the river called the Jordan.
Others said he was last known to be staying
in the south with a community
of prophets and preachers in a place
called Qumran, about twenty-five miles
from Jerusalem.
There, not far from Qumran,
where the Jordan
finally empties its water into the Dead Sea,
John and his disciples were calling
the people to ready themselves
for the coming day of God's rule.
Others of the caravan said
John was preaching,
"There is no king but God
and you are under his rule."
"John is not the only preacher saying it,"
they said, "but he is a convincing preacher."
Others reported to Jesus
that they understood John was also seen
somewhere between both these places
near the Samarian countryside.

Some said John was last seen
in the Valley of Jezreel.
Others said he was reported
near the brook of Kerith.
"No matter," thought Jesus,
"I shall go to the east to the place
where the Jordan is filled
by the Galilee Lake
and follow the river south
until I find John and his disciples."

By following this route
Jesus found himself much alone.
He would pause to rest now and then
by some river overlook.
He was quiet before the beauty he saw.
He noticed that the river had many moods.
In the morning, the water glistened
in the first rays of the sunlight.

40

And by night, the moon painted
a path of light from bank to bank.
In some places the water
tumbled and whirled
in rushing splashes and crashing roars.
Sometimes Jesus came to a level place
where the water spread out into
a quiet collecting place
and all was peaceful and calm.
By morning and night,
Jesus washed himself in its water.
As the water cooled and cleaned his skin,
he prayed the prayer of his fathers,
"Create in me a clean heart, O God,
and renew a right spirit within me."

"Has John the Baptist been here?"
Jesus asked a lonely shepherd one day.
"Not for several months," he was told.

41

"He is in the south," Jesus was told by
some boys fishing by the river.
"Unless King Herod has had him killed
by now," one boy added.
"Some of his enemies came to get evidence
that he was arousing the people
against the government of King Herod.
The people would not speak against John,"
the boy went on, "but the spies tried to
get us to lie about the Baptizer's words."

As night came on, the fifth night of his
southward journey, Jesus' mind was troubled
by the news the fishing boys had given.
"Why do my people refuse to hear
the good men who speak out for God?"
he asked himself.
"Why have my people, so blessed by God,
refused to hear the truth?
Why have they killed God's prophets?"

Jesus tossed in a light sleep that night.
Sometimes there were dangers
in serving God.
Surely John was strong.
But could not one be strong
and still be afraid?
How brave would one have to be
to stand with God against a king?
Jesus thought he had had troubled dreams
when he awoke by the Jordan.
He was troubled of mind.
He knew he must hurry to meet John
and to warn him that he was in danger.

42

The Meeting

Jesus was troubled by the news that
King Herod was trying to get evidence
against John so he could arrest him for
disloyalty to the government.
Jesus determined to speed up his walking.
"I have been so busy with my own thoughts
and so taken by the beauty
of the country," Jesus admitted,
"that I have not been going fast enough
in my search to find my cousin."
As he followed the river by the curve
closest to the city of Jericho,
he came upon more travelers, and of each
he asked for new information about
John's whereabouts.
It was soon explained
that John often came to teach and baptize
at Beth-abara, a place by the river only a
short walking distance from Jericho.
It was also made clear
that for several weeks
John had not been to Beth-abara
but was staying farther south.
"I hear he is staying at Qumran,"
a priest returning to Jericho explained.
"But when he comes to Beth-abara
with his disciples, news spreads so quickly
that in only a few hours
a great crowd will gather to hear him.

"Would that the people were so quick to hear
their own priests as they are
to listen to John."
"Is John popular with the people then?"
Jesus wanted to know.
"Ever so popular," the priest explained.
"People come from miles around to hear him.
And they are not disappointed in him.
He is a sight to see.
He is a courageous man.
Even now, there are people camping
at Beth-abara, hoping
for the Baptizer to come.
His disciples were increasing daily, until ..."
The priest paused as though not to say more.
"Until what?" Jesus pressed for more news.
"Until John started condemning some of us
and the king started to be worried
by his preaching."
The priest leaned over to shake the dust
off his robe. He looked up at Jesus.
Jesus seemed harmless enough,
and friendly too, so the priest continued.
"Well, King Herod has acted unwisely,"
he said.
"John the Baptizer isn't raising an army.
He isn't recruiting soldiers.
He is only calling people to be religious.
He is warning them that God
will punish wrongdoing.
John says we Jews can never be
a free people until we surrender to
God's rule even as we have to Herod's.
That much is good religion."

44

Jesus nodded. "Is Herod afraid
that the people will hail John as a king
or Messiah to free the people
from Rome's army?" he asked.
"Would that John were our Savior!"
The priest hit his hand with his fist.
"Many of us hoped he would raise an army.
But he would not hear of it.
We priests asked John,
'Who are you?' We hoped he would say,
'The leader, Christ.'
Instead he said he was not Christ
or the hoped-for prophet.
All he would say of himself was:
'I am one who preaches in the countryside,
making our country ready for the Lord God.
Leave your wrongdoing, and
love that which is true and right.
Turn away from sin.
Give up all that keeps you
from serving God as your King.'"
"Were others hoping he would lead
our people to freedom?" Jesus pressed.
"Yes, many hoped so. But the only hope
John gives us is that a Savior
is even now among us and we know him not.
I heard him say this myself.
You see," he continued, "Herod believes
John is secretly speaking about himself.
Though John denies it, Herod will not
be put off. If the King can arrange it,
he will surely arrest John.
The King is frightened of the talk
of a new kingdom for God."

45

Jesus nodded. The priest continued,
"In the meantime, John has insulted us too.
He charges that our brotherhood of priests
does nothing to stop wrongdoing
and that we are even teaching people
to disobey God by
our religious rules. Imagine!
No wonder some are turning against him.
I heard his insults myself.
Some religious leaders thought
they would go along with his movement
and see if we might not rally around John
to drive out the army of Rome.
As they came forward to be baptized,
John gave them a public tongue-lashing.
He called them 'a lot of snakes'
and asked if they were sincere.
That man doesn't care what he says
to anyone, believe me.
John loves God above everything."

"He is only afraid of failing God,"
Jesus said. "Well, I've been glad
to talk with you," Jesus smiled.
"Let us pray that we may be delivered
from the anger of God
if those who claim to be his special people
do not start to live
by his truth and his law!"
The priest looked Jesus straight in the eye.
"You sound like John. That is what he says."
"Sir," said Jesus, "I thank you
for your compliment."
"But," laughed the priest,
"you don't look like him.
John is growing thin from not eating.
His great camel's hair coat
now is too big for him.
He does not shave and . . . well, he looks
like a wild prophet of the wilderness,
as Elijah of old must have looked."
"Then," Jesus said, "he is more interested
in serving God than in being popular.
May God bless him.
May God protect him.
And may God bless his truth to all
who will learn from him."
"Do you think he is the prophet?
Is he the Christ?" asked the priest.
"We need true prophets." He shook his head.
"Are you his disciple? Are you a disciple
of John?" the priest asked.
"As of now," Jesus answered slowly,
"I must say that my one wish is
to be used for God's glory.

"God is my King. And," Jesus added,
"I go to see John to decide
if God will speak to me through him."
"Then go in peace," said the priest.
"And may God speak to you."
"Peace," Jesus replied.

It was late in the day when Jesus
arrived at the community of Qumran.
Jesus walked up to the main building,
passing the tower at the northwest corner.
He pounded on the great wooden door
with his stout walking stick.
He heard the echo of his knock
bounce off the walls inside.
"I am seeking John, my cousin,
known as a prophet and the Baptizer.
Is he here? I have walked all the way
from Nazareth of Galilee to see him,"
Jesus announced. "Is he here?"
A man closed the door as quietly
as he had opened it.
Jesus waited, and waited, and waited.
Then he heard, faintly at first,
then with certainty, the door squeak
until it stood wide open,
and in the light of an oil lamp stood John.
His familiar face was somewhat older
and was now framed by a massive beard.
"Jesus! Jesus! Jesus! Jesus!"
John's big voice repeated.
He quickly placed his little lamp
on a table by the door, and the two men
embraced again and again.

48

"I feared for your life, John," Jesus said.
"I have heard Herod would destroy you."
"Herod!" John's voice did not show respect.
"I do not fear Herod.
He can only kill my body.
I only fear God, who really rules
life and death."
"Then peace, Cousin John.
I have longed to see you.
I have longed to talk with you.
Praise be to God. I have found you."
"And peace be returned to you, Jesus."
John beamed.
"I have been looking for you to come.
Some months ago I received your message
from my disciple Samuel who was returning
through Nazareth from the north.

49

"He said you were soon to leave all
to take up the service of God.
He said you might come to see me.
Will you stay with me awhile, Jesus?
Will you stay with me awhile?"
John wanted to know.
"If I will be welcomed. Yes.
If I will not stop your important work."
John put his arm around Jesus
and led him into the dark hallway,
closing the door behind him.

"Stop my work?" John grinned.
"With you here, it can really begin.
In all our childhood and youth
you were the leader, Jesus.
I was the follower. Perhaps
after we have prayed together for
awhile, God will show us what is next."
"That is what I need," Jesus nodded,
"God to show me what is next."
"Then welcome seven times and
seven times seven," John said as they
started to climb the great staircase.
"I will show you to a room
that can be yours as long as you stay,
and then take you to the great hall
where the Brothers of our fellowship
will enter into prayer together."
"God be praised," said Jesus, already
refreshed by the strong faith of John.
"And Jesus be blessed," said John,
who from his childhood had found
his hero to be Jesus.

From the Making of Bread

In the morning, after a restful sleep,
Jesus rose early to kneel by his bed.
He continued to pray until he was ready
for whatever the new day might hold.
Then Jesus met John.
Together they went into the great hall
where the men gathered quietly
to eat a simple breakfast.
The long rows of tables were crowded.
But seeing John and his guest, the men
pushed closer together to make room
for them. "There is always room
for another in the family of God,"
the man next to Jesus whispered.
Jesus smiled and nodded his thanks.
Jesus and John sat side by side.
Before eating, everyone joined
in the singing of psalms
and the saying of prayers.
While they ate, Jesus looked down the rows
to notice how simply each man was dressed
and how friendly was each smile.
Jesus was greeted by their nods.
"They know little of me," Jesus thought,
"but they are making me welcome.
Where God is known as Father
it is always like that—
all are brothers in God's family."
After breakfast, John took Jesus on a tour

to see the walled community.
"John," said Jesus, "you are growing thin.
I noticed you are eating little.
Are you going without food
for a special reason?"
"Yes," John explained, "I am fasting
as a way to keep aware of God
or I may be tempted to give in
to King Herod and stop my preaching."
Jesus put his arm on John's shoulder.
"But, John," he said, showing concern,
"do not fast to the place of sickness.
You need strength of body to serve God
as well as strength of mind."

John changed the subject with a smile.
"Outside the walls," he said,
"the Brothers of Qumran grow their grain,
and in here it is stored." He pointed to
a storage room filled with bags of wheat.
"And here is the mill where
the grain is ground into flour,"
John explained. "Next I will show you
the baking ovens where
the flour dough becomes bread.
The Brothers here have built this whole
community, wall and all, stone by stone."
"Do the Brothers each have work to do?"
Jesus wanted to know.
"Yes," replied John, "every man who lives
here must work. Some work in the fields,
some make dishes and pots in the clay
workshop, some work in the kitchen, some
are builders, and some study the Law of God.

"I will show you the study hall
where the scrolls of the Law and
the words of the prophets are kept.
Some of the Brothers make new scrolls
and make new copies of the Scriptures
as their work. And some go out to preach."
"Yes," smiled Jesus, "that is your
great work. Tell me, Cousin, how is it
God has blessed your preaching?
You are known everywhere."
"My dear Jesus," said John,
"God is at work. The people are eager
to hear of God. One has only to speak
about God to the people and tell them
what God wants of them
and the crowds gather.
I think the priests have made a mistake
to talk always about what God has done
in the long ago."
"You are right, John," said Jesus.
"The Father God is at work today.
Why do the priests point
so often to the past?
Some seem to talk as if God were dead."

"I agree," John replied. "While some
have preached to recruit a Jewish army
to drive out the Romans, I say
stop the way of war.
Leave all feelings of hate behind.
Love all. Join the family of God."
"They that kill with swords will die
by swords," Jesus agreed.
"But," Jesus went on, "do you ask
the people to leave their homes
and jobs to live in separate communities
like this one you have just shown to me?"
Jesus' brow was furrowed.
"John!" Jesus pressed his question
by tapping his finger on the wall.
"Does God want us to escape evil
by running away from the world's troubles
into pleasant places like this one?
To refresh oneself for a little while, yes.
But to live a whole life away
from the people—
surely that is not best!"
"I have thought it important," replied John,
"to call people away from the troubles
which keep them from living for God."
"You are right to be aware of God,"
answered Jesus. "You are right to seek
to live to please God.
But I cannot think it the best way—
to live off by oneself
away from the people's needs.
Surely, God will help those who love him
overcome evil with good even in the cities.
John, many people live in the cities.

54

"Why not go there to preach?
Surely, the Father wants us to be a light
in the dark places.
God calls us to be helping the poor
and the sick, and to be showing
God's way for today's problems."
John turned slowly and looked squarely
at Jesus. Both were silent.
Jesus' face was calm and sure.
John's look was full of questions.
Jesus broke the quiet
by a friendly nudge with his fist
on John's arm. "Is this not the
Scriptures' teaching?" he asked.
"I must think of this," said John.
"I must consider this. I have heard
of your work around Nazareth. I have
heard that besides working with wood
with Joseph, you have kept busy
visiting with sick people, teaching
children, collecting food from your
neighbors to share with the poor."
"I have," said Jesus, "and found God
to bless such service.
We cannot run away from the people
or from their problems.
I say God wants us to go to them,
wherever they are. He wants us
to make known the good news that
God is near at all times to help, that
God wants his kingdom to be everywhere."

John took Jesus' arm and led him
toward the shade by the kitchen.

There, the two men sat on a stone seat
with their separate thoughts.
As they sat thinking, the Qumran Brothers
assigned to mix the dough for bread
were busy at their task in the kitchen.
Some of the loaves were already puffing up.
The dough increased until it filled
the baking dish and ran over on the table.
The two men watched quietly.
"John," cried Jesus, inspired with an idea.
"Look at the bread! Think of the yeast.
Where do the bakers put the yeast?
Where, John? Where?"
John answered slowly, "In the dough
to make it rise. In the dough."
"Then," asked Jesus, "why not put your
disciples to work among the people showing
them how to serve God in their
everyday living? Cannot God use you
to change the people,
to change our nation,
as he uses yeast to change
flour dough into bread?"
"Your ideas always stir me, Jesus,"
said John. "Even from such simple acts
as the making of bread,
you find lessons about God and his kingdom.
Are you saying God's rule must be
in the lives of the people
wherever they are?"
"I am," said Jesus.
"And I am saying our Heavenly Father
will use those who know themselves to be
his children to spread his kingdom among

56

all the people and to change lives;
to change their homes and communities."
John was silent. He was thoughtful.

"I hear the carpenters pounding,"
said Jesus. "Will they let me help?"
"I will let you help them build
the roof over the new sleeping rooms
if you will promise to talk with me
again this afternoon," John said.
"And I will talk with you this afternoon,"
Jesus answered, "if you will promise to
take me with you when you go to preach
and baptize on your next trip."
"Agreed. But that must wait for awhile,
Jesus." John was serious. "That
must wait now. I hear God speaking to me
through you and I must learn more from you,
for surely God has sent you to me."
Jesus climbed the ladder to join
the other carpenters.
"Yes, our Father God has brought
us together, John," Jesus called down.
John smiled up at him. "Peace," he said.
"And God's peace be with you," Jesus replied.

Into the Water

"I'm looking for Jesus, Brother David.
Have you seen him?" John asked.
"He is in the great hall, Brother John,"
David answered. "He is upstairs."
"I am going preaching tomorrow.
I wanted to ask Jesus to go with me again,"
said John.
"He has been going with you often,"
David observed. "That is too bad for me.
Jesus is a good carpenter, and we are
starting to build some tables tomorrow.
We could use him here, John."
John raised his eyebrows, pretending
to be surprised. "Then," he laughed,
"you are no longer able
to do good carpenter work by yourselves?"
"Oh, it is not that," David smiled.
"It is the talks we have with Jesus that
make our work so pleasant. To be around
Jesus is to know God is near.
All of the men seek out his company.
All of them are better for having
his example among us."
"Yes," agreed John, "he has been for us
as yeast is for a lump of dough."
"Some of our Brothers are even talking
of becoming his disciples," David added.
"His ideas excite and rally the men."
John started up the stone stairway.

At the top, he called back to David,
who had started up the stairs after him.
"I think Jesus is explaining the Scriptures
to some of our Brothers now. Jesus seems
to know more about the Scriptures
than the students of the Law.
They are always asking him
to explain *this* or *that*."
As they reached the great hall, John and
David were side by side. They were not
surprised by the crowd gathered there or
that Jesus was in the center of it.
"The hour is growing late, my brothers,"
Jesus was saying. "We must
be getting ready for sleep."
"Then," said one of the leaders of the
community, "we must beg of Jesus
one more favor. Jesus, please lead us
in our evening prayers."
As all the Brothers knelt down,
the rustle of the robes and the squeaking
of benches moved into the deepest kind
of quiet known, when men pray hard.

After a time, Jesus' voice spoke quietly.
"Our Father, who art in heaven,
Hallowed be thy name.
Thy kingdom come,
Thy will be done,
On earth among the people even
as it is done in heaven.
Give us this day our daily bread;
Forgive us this day all wrong we have done.
Help us to forgive all
who may have wronged us.
Protect us from all desire to do wrong.
Deliver us when we give in to any kind
of evil. For all the world is thine.
All glory and all power is thine.
All love is from thee. Keep us alive
to the way of love forever. Amen."

After a long silence, the men rose—
one by one—and left the great hall.
When Jesus rose to go, all the rest
had left. John was kneeling by the door.
When he saw Jesus coming out,
John rose to meet him.
"Peace, Jesus," John greeted him.
"God is in you. To be with you
is to be with God." Without waiting for
an answer he continued. "And will you not
preach tomorrow, Jesus? Will you not
preach to the people?"
"I will gladly leave to go to the Jordan
with you tomorrow, John," Jesus replied.
"But I will not preach.
Tomorrow is the day I have waited for.

"I will hear you preach again, and
I think God will give me the answer
I have been waiting for. Tomorrow
God will use you
to make clear for me his way."

By the time John, Jesus, and a small group
of John's disciples arrived at Beth-abara,
not far from Jericho, word had spread
that he was coming. A big crowd was already
waiting. As they came near the river,
the people gathered around excitedly
to see the Baptizer.
In due time, John began talking with them.
"If you have turned your life over to God,"
he began in a booming voice,
"your neighbors will know it. If you plant
an olive tree, the olives at harvest time
that fill the limbs are proof that
the tree is really an olive tree.
A tree is known by its fruit.
And if you are a child of God,"
John went on,
"your good deeds and honest living
will show all that you belong to God."
"But," one man argued back,
"we are born into a religious family
in a religious nation.
We trace our family all the way
back to Abraham, father of our country."
"Abraham's goodness is not yours,"
answered John.
"Everyone must respond to God for himself."
Then another of the crowd asked,

"O Prophet, tell us, what should we do
to show we are God's children and that we
love God as did our Father Abraham?"
John remembered many of his conversations
with Jesus. But Jesus' ideas were now
clearly his own, too. John spoke with
strength for he was sure of his answers.
"The man with two shirts, let him give one
of them to him without any. And if you
have food and find someone who is hungry,
share food with him generously."
A tax collector wanted some advice.
"Don't take any money
you are not supposed to collect,"
John explained. "Do not steal from anyone."
Then some soldiers asked, "And what of us?"
John told them, "Do not bully the weak,
and do not be cruel."
John explained that when one knows himself
to be a part of God's family, he gives
up everything that God cannot praise.
The people were greatly moved by
John's sincerity. His words made them
forget everything but God.
"God is ready to welcome you into his
own kingdom of peace," John invited.
"Come and let me lower you into the water
as a way to show everyone that you really
want to live for God as a part of his
kingdom where all men are brothers."
John laid aside his great camel's hair
coat, for it was warm.
John bent over to fasten his cloth garment
tightly and walked into the water.

Many of the people knelt to pray
for God's forgiveness.
A great silence fell over the people.
John lifted his head toward the sky.
"Bless those who come into the water,
O God," he prayed. "As their bodies are
washed, clean their thoughts and receive
them into thy family of love and service."
John turned around.
He was surprised to see Jesus coming
into the water toward him.
"You must baptize me, Man of God," Jesus
said to John. "I would be covered with
water. I, too, want to live only for God."
John trembled. He did not know what to say.
"No, no, Jesus!" John's voice was weak.
"I am not worthy to baptize you.
Instead I want you to baptize me."

63

"Please, Man of God!" Jesus insisted.
"Help me to know that I belong to God."
Jesus' look was ever so serious.
John knew then he must do as Jesus asked.
The two men prayed hard.
They were aware of nothing but God.
Then John put one hand behind Jesus' neck
and the other hand on his chest and slowly
lowered Jesus all the way into the water.

Later, some said it thundered then.
Some said they heard a great voice.
Some said they heard nothing.
Still others said at that moment they were
certain, as they were never before,
that God was with them.
John said nothing until the next day.
The Baptizer was with two of his disciples
when Jesus passed by them.
"There goes God's Son!"
John pointed toward Jesus.
"He is our Savior from God!"
But John's disciples did not seem
really surprised. "We have wondered about
Jesus, for we have known
he was not like other men," they said.
"How blessed you are, John," his disciples
said. "God has been using you to prepare
the people to receive his own Son, Jesus."

In the Steps of John

"What is next for you, Jesus?" John asked.
"I must leave, John, to be all alone
with God." Jesus replied.
"Jesus," said John, "will you take
my disciples to be your own disciples?
Many of them know you are sent
from God and would follow you."
"One step at a time," Jesus smiled.
"I must be alone now for awhile."
"Then we but wait for word from you,
and we will do as you say," John replied.
"My dear John." Jesus put his arm
around him. "How I have been refreshed
by your love. Thanks be to God
for your life and work."
John lowered his eyes: "I am the one
made strong by your love."
The two friends prayed for God's peace.
Then John watched as Jesus started walking
toward the south and the lonely countryside.
It was more than forty days
before Jesus returned to Beth-abara.
His skin was tanned. His body was thinner.
His mind now was sure.
His eyes were bright. His face was firm.
He walked tall and straight.
As Jesus came to the place where he had
entered the water with John the Baptizer,
the sun was low in the sky.

He sat down and leaned against
a tree to rest. His thoughts were broken
as a shadow of a familiar figure
shut out the rays of the setting sun.
"Jesus, is it you? Jesus!
How much I have thought of you.
Praise God you have come!
Are you going to take over now?"
Jesus jumped to his feet
to greet the man standing over him.
"Why, it is Brother David, carpenter
of Qumran. Peace to you from God, David.

"How good it is to see you. And how is
John?" Jesus' face spread into a big
smile at the thought of his respected friend.
"Have you not heard?" David wiped his face
on his sleeve to hide some tears.
"They have taken the Baptizer, Jesus.
They have arrested John.
Did you not know?" David asked.
"No," replied Jesus, "I have been alone
for some forty days."
They sat down together by the tree.
Jesus' face showed his pain.
"So King Herod has taken him."
The quiet that followed was long.
Each in his own way prayed for John.
"John's disciples have been carrying
on his work," Brother David explained.
"The Brothers are taking turns.
The news that John
was put in prison has even increased
the number of people who come here.
The people love John even more now.
We baptized fourteen more men today.
But some of us have been hoping you would
start to preach in John's place.
Tomorrow, another even larger crowd
will come. You will see, Jesus!
You must preach tomorrow."
Jesus thought for a moment and
shook his head. He spoke firmly.
"No," he said. "I cannot preach
here tomorrow."
Brother David's face
showed his disappointment.

"The best way," Jesus continued,
"to serve God now and to honor John
is to carry on his work.
Let John's disciples work harder to
tell everyone hereabouts that God is
busy here. Let them point to changing
lives as the evidence that God is working."
"Then what will you do?" David wanted
to know of Jesus. "Where will you go?"
"I must go to my home country of Galilee,
gather some disciples of my own, and
start to spread the good news
that Herod cannot stop God.
I, too, will preach and baptize
the people, but in Galilee!"
"Then you think John's followers
should carry on here at Beth-abara?"
asked David.
"Yes, here and in Jericho, Jerusalem,
and every place. Let all John's followers
become for the people hereabouts as
the yeast is for changing and increasing
the bread dough." Jesus was feeling better.
"And I," he added, "will go north to
Galilee to take up my own ministry."
"Some of the followers of John are afraid,"
David confessed. "They fear that Herod
will not stop with putting John in prison.
Some say the King will kill John. And so
some of the disciples see their lives
in danger, too. If Herod is so afraid
of our teachings that he took our leader,
what will he do if our members
increase even faster without John?"

"Brother David! Brother David!"
Jesus assured the carpenter.
"Take a lesson from John. He was not
afraid of Herod's power.
Fear only God."
Jesus had been pulling on some weeds
while he talked. He looked down at his hand.
The ripe seedpods had opened to spill
the tiny seeds into the palm of his hand.
"Look here, Brother David," said Jesus
as he moved the seeds around in his palm.
"How shall these seeds grow into plants?"
"The seed will become a plant," David
reasoned out loud. "When it is covered
with dirt, it dies as a seed to live on
in a growing plant."
"And," Jesus completed the idea,
"do not fear to die. If John must die,
God will give him a bigger life, not only
in heaven, but with more followers here."
Jesus lifted himself to his knees.
"Anyhow, Brother David," Jesus grinned,
"look how little the mustard seed is.
But what a great plant it becomes!"
"True. Your words sound true."
David nodded. "I understand.
We started with only a few followers
and God has already blessed our work
with many disciples."
Jesus stood tall and stretched.
"Do you start back for Qumran tonight,
David? Or will you join me in prayers
and spend the night near the Jordan?"
David motioned that he was planning to stay.

The two left the road to go toward
the river bank to find a place to camp.

The trip north along the Jordan was as
pleasant for Jesus as his walk southward
had been some months before
when he was first looking for John.
He thought about John and prayed for him
as he walked. And he decided that he
would go north first to Capernaum
by the lake of Galilee about twenty-three
miles from his boyhood town of Nazareth.
"I think I shall go to the synagogue
in Capernaum first to see if some members
of that congregation are already acting
as good witnesses to God.
I might find some disciples from the men
of the synagogue," Jesus thought.

In Capernaum on the Sabbath day,
Jesus went to the synagogue.
While the worshipers gathered, Jesus
visited with the men waiting outside.
They were talking about
John the Baptizer.
"News of his arrest has traveled fast,"
Jesus thought.
"Have you ever heard John preach?"
the men asked Jesus.
"I have heard him often," Jesus said.
"I spent several months with him,"
Jesus explained. "John is a prophet for God.
He is not afraid.

70

"He is one to stand up even to kings."
The men were excited to hear that
Jesus had been so recently with
the famous preacher. One of them
left the group to go inside and returned
shortly with the leader of the congregation.
"Will you speak to us this morning?"
he invited Jesus. "John is much admired
by some of our members. I am sure everyone
would be glad to hear you speak today."

The response to Jesus' sermon was
enthusiastic. "An inspired preacher,"
the people said of him.
After that, Jesus became friends with
a number of young men who sought him out
to learn from him. In these friendships,
Jesus began to see which of the
Capernaum men he might ask
to be his disciples.
So it was that Jesus began his own
ministry in the steps of John—preaching,
teaching, and looking for disciples.

Twelve Learners

Word soon spread of the great new preacher.
Jesus was invited to speak often in the
synagogues near the Lake of Galilee.
So popular was he that he decided
to return to his boyhood town of Nazareth
and preach there about God's kingdom.
But the people of Nazareth did not
consider Jesus a great prophet at all.
"Was he not little Jesus? He is only a
carpenter pretending to be a prophet.
Why does he pretend to have a
special message from God?"
It was not a happy homecoming for Jesus.
He knew he was not going to be welcomed
everywhere or believed in by everyone.
Jesus was glad to visit again
with his mother, his brothers James,
Joses, Judas, and Simon,
and with his younger sisters.
But even that was a sad time.
"We all miss Joseph," Rabbi Ben Eli
told Jesus. "He was a good man,
and he died praising God."
Jesus visited again some of the sick
he used to help when he lived in Nazareth.
Only they seemed glad to see him.
Jesus prayed for them. Some so believed
that God had sent Jesus home to help them
that they became completely well.

But apart from that success
the trip was a disappointment.
At Rabbi Ben Eli's invitation, Jesus
agreed to read the Scriptures in his
boyhood synagogue at the Sabbath service.
Jesus read from the prophet Isaiah.
When he had finished reading, Jesus said:
"I am making this prophet's
words come true."
The congregation whispered together.
They said: "Him? He was nice as a
little boy, and a good carpenter.
But how can a carpenter get such
big ideas to think God is using him
to make the Scriptures come true?
What a boastful fool!
Do not listen to his wild claims!"
"Let us chase him out of town," some said.

Some would even have thrown Jesus
over a cliff, but he escaped from them
and hurried back to the Lake
of Galilee area. There Jesus deepened
his friendship with some of the men
he had met in the Capernaum synagogue.
When he was not teaching or visiting
the sick, he sometimes went with these
friends in their boats on the lake.
They had long talks while they fished.
Jesus liked them very much.
They greatly respected Jesus.
Simon and his brother Andrew were
favorites of Jesus. Jesus also liked
James and John,
the sons of the fisherman Zebedee.
They were Simon's partners
and got along well together.
Jesus had explained carefully that God's
call required one to give his life
in service to others.
"I do not intend to live off in a
special community," Jesus told them.
"My place is with the people, helping them.
He is greatest in God's kingdom
who helps others the most."

One day Jesus, now becoming famous
in Galilee, was followed by a crowd
of people hoping to hear him speak.
Jesus was walking by the waterside
and saw Simon and his partners
washing the fish nets.
"I need a boat from which to preach.

74

"May I borrow your boat, Simon?"
Jesus asked.
"Of course, Man of God," Simon answered
as he motioned to his brother Andrew,
and to James and John,
to come listen to Jesus.
Simon pushed the boat a little way
out in the water. As Jesus spoke, the
crowd grew until there were more people
than Simon could count.
When Jesus had finished teaching
about God, the people refused
to leave, hoping he would say more.
"When I hear you tell of God's way
for those who love and serve him,"
Simon said, "it makes me think that
being a fisherman, as was my father
before me, is a waste of my time.
I, too, should be about God's business."
"You told me," Jesus answered,
"that you had considered following
John the Baptizer. Why didn't you?"
"I must keep active," Simon smiled.
"I love to be around the people.
I like to keep busy too much
to shut myself away somewhere."
"Come, Simon and Andrew," said Jesus,
"take me fishing so
we can be alone to talk."
James and John followed in their boat.
"We have not been catching any fish today,"
Simon complained.
Andrew raised the sail
and they headed away from the shore.

They talked for a long time about
God's plan for Simon and for Andrew.
"Your friends, James and John, talk
as you do," Jesus said. "You four
are so much alike in your thoughts,
I am sure God would bless you as a team
in his service. I have been wondering,"
said Jesus, "if you would join me
in showing that God is busy right
now bringing about his rule in the lives
of those who turn to him."
"Would you accept us as your disciples,
Master?" Simon looked surprised
that Jesus would even consider them.
"Oh, Master," said Simon, "I am not
worthy to be your disciple. I am
full of sin."
"Let God be the judge of that,"
Jesus assured him.
Just then the nets, so long empty,
began to fill with fish.
"Look sharply there, James! The fish,
John!" Simon shouted. "Pull in the nets."
All four worked quickly.
Jesus jumped up and helped Andrew.
"That's enough, men," Simon ordered.
"No more fish or we will sink the boats."
They all were wiping their faces and puffing.
"With you, Jesus," Simon said, lowering
his head, "even the fish come to my net.
Everything goes best when I am with you."
"Then," said Jesus laughing, "from now on,
will you leave fishing from a boat
to fish for men with me on the shore?"

Jesus looked into the eyes of the men.
"God be with you," said Jesus.
"Peace," the fishermen replied.
The fish flopped in the bottom of the boat.

Some months later Simon said:
"There are now twelve of us who have
left everything to learn from you, Jesus.
How many more disciples will you choose?"
"I think twelve will do," said Jesus.
"You are a special group,"
Jesus smiled. "Your influence can be
far-reaching and help to spread
God's good news across the land,"
Jesus went on. "You, Matthew, are you
sorry you gave up tax collecting?"
Matthew shook his head. "Never, Lord!"
"And what of you, my Sons of Thunder?"
Jesus asked. He looked at the brothers
James and John to whom
he had given this funny name.
All the disciples grinned at this fun.
"You will make good preachers with
your big voices," Simon cried out.
Everyone laughed at the onetime fishermen.
James blushed and stirred the campfire.
"Seriously, Lord," Andrew spoke out,
"you are my only Master!"
Jesus' mood became more serious now.
"Then are you still determined to stay
with me, Philip?" Jesus asked, continuing
his questions. His eyes went from one
to another. "Bartholomew?"
"Still with you, Master," he answered.

"Thomas?" Jesus asked.
"Till God rules in every life," he said.
"And how about you,
James, son of Alphaeus,
and you, Thaddaeus? Have you any doubts?"
Jesus' look was very serious now.
"None," they said, shaking their heads.
"And you, my other Simon, you who were a
member of the Zealot party wanting war
. . . has my talk of a kingdom of peace
bothered you?"
"I am with you completely, Teacher,"
Simon the Zealot assured him.
"And what of you, Judas Iscariot?"
"I will never leave you, Jesus,"
he answered. "Never!"
Jesus turned to his friend Simon, the
fisherman, whom he had nicknamed Peter,
which means rock, because he had such
great strength. "And you, Simon, my
Rock," he smiled, "are you ready to go
back to your fishing?"
"I miss nothing when I am with you,
Lord," he said.

Simon Peter crossed his legs to get
comfortable for he wanted to say something.
"Master," he said, "we have been going
with you everywhere around Galilee.
Your crowds are bigger than those that
heard John the Baptizer. And at your word
people change their whole way of life.
People meet you and know themselves
to be sons of God. And . . ." Simon Peter

swallowed to hold back his excitement,
"we see lame people touch you—
believing you have been sent by God—
and they are healed.
We saw a miracle the other week
when thousands of people, on the
hillside, were hungry. When the little
boy with his bread and fish offered
them to you to feed the people, we ended
up with everyone sharing his food. So
much was left over we could gather up
thirty baskets full to give to the poor."
"What are you getting at, Simon Peter?"
Jesus wanted to know.
"Well, we know God is in you, for he
blesses what you do and he answers
your prayers. But when will you use us
to do miracles and to change people's
lives and to baptize the people, too?"
Peter was speaking fast now and
emphasizing each word with his hands.
"How long is it going to be
before we are able to do what you do?
When are we going to work on our own?"
"Will you always be impatient, Peter?"
Jesus asked. "Let me ask you a question
since you have put so many to me.
Can a blind man lead another blind man
safely past a big ditch?"
Simon Peter looked around thoughtfully.
Since he did not answer, Jesus went on.
"Won't they both fall into the hole unless
one can see where to lead the other?"
Peter understood. He blushed.

"Please keep learning and
try to be steady as a rock, Simon.
Remember that a disciple is not ready
to be a teacher until he has learned
all the teacher has to teach him!"
"Oh," stuttered Simon, embarrassed, "I was
only thinking about the others
who are getting anxious to share
in your great work on their own."
"Simon, Simon," Jesus laughed, "why
do you bother yourself worrying about
the tiny splinter in your brother's eye
when you have a big log in your own?"
Everyone grinned at Peter's embarrassment,
but they knew Jesus was speaking to them
also. "How easy it is to learn from
Jesus," the men said to each other as
they put out the campfire. "He wraps so
many of his lessons in a good laugh!"

So the disciples of Jesus continued to
learn from him every day—for they were
eager to be like their teacher who made
God seem very near to them.

Where Will Herod Stop?

Jesus was busy.
The disciples were around Jesus trying
to help him see the important people,
the most needy people. They were not
aware of the children or the fathers
and mothers with their babies in their
arms on the edge of the crowd.
"Children aren't very important,"
they thought. The disciples didn't think
the children should be allowed near.
"They will bother Jesus,"
Matthew explained.
But Jesus saw his disciples
sending the children away.
"Jesus is too busy to see you," they said.
"What are you doing there, Bartholomew?"
Jesus called out. Jesus was unhappy.
Everyone knew by the tone of his voice.
"Why do you send the children away? Let
them come to me, for God's kingdom belongs
to them, too! Just because they are little,"
Jesus went on, waving to the small ones
to come to him, "doesn't mean they are
not of great importance to God."
The disciples did not like to have Jesus
unhappy with them. So they asked everyone
else to step back to let the children into
the center of the circle. That made
Jesus happy. He talked with the children.

They climbed all over his lap when he
sat down. He took time for each one.
"Even the children take to him," Judas
chuckled. Following Jesus' example, each
of the disciples started to pay attention
to the children. Jesus told them that
on each of their trips they should put
their hands on the heads of the children
and bless them in God's name.

Bartholomew walked faster to catch up
to Thomas. They had bid the people
good-bye and were going to their camping
spot. "Jesus said he had some things to
say to us," Bartholomew smiled. "I guess
we may hear about children tonight."
"I don't think so," Thomas answered.
"I think Jesus knows when we have learned
our lesson." Then Thomas went on. "Those
who think Jesus is just another John the
Baptist don't understand him, do they?"

82

He was thinking hard. "The kingdom which
God is bringing in through Jesus is really
far more than the Baptizer had in mind.
Whoever thought in the old days that
women and children were as important
to God as men? Jesus has almost as many
women followers as men. And now children,
too! He means it when he says,
'God loves all.'
It is a new day and a new way!"
Bartholomew agreed, adding: "I still think
Jesus will talk about children tonight."
Thomas shrugged his shoulders twice as
if to say, "We shall see. We shall see."

"Is everyone here?" Jesus asked,
pretending not to see Simon Peter.
The disciples knew from the twinkle
of his eye that Jesus was getting ready
to do something important.
"I'm right here!" Simon Peter announced.
"Oh, there you are, my Rock." Jesus smiled.
"For a long time you have been such good
learners that I think it is about time
for the students to start copying their
teacher. I knew you especially wouldn't
want to miss that news, Peter, since you
asked about my plans so long ago."
Simon Peter smiled good-naturedly. All
of his friends were calling him "Peter" now.
Jesus had first called him that in fun because
the name meant rock.
Peter was strong and steady as a rock.
He liked being called this name.

"Two Simons in one group are one too many
anyhow," he thought. "I'll let the Zealot
keep the name Simon. My new one came
from Jesus with my changed life."
Jesus turned all seriousness and
the men settled down around the campfire.
"Awhile back," Jesus recalled, "Simon
Peter wanted to know when I would send
you out to do as you have seen me doing.
I am pleased by all our invitations
to preach, by the great crowds of people
who follow us everywhere, and by the
miracles of God in answer to our prayers.
The time has come for us to put
the yeast to work in the dough.
It is time for each of you to minister
in the towns and villages on your own."
The twelve men were excited by the news.
"I don't think we have enough money in
the treasury right now for a lot of travel
expense," Judas, the treasurer, said.
"Will we be able to heal the sick?"
Thomas wanted to know. "Will we baptize
in God's name or yours, Master?"
Everyone started to talk.
"Can I travel with my brother John?"
James asked.
Jesus stood up and motioned for them
to be quiet. "All questions will be
answered in time," he said.
"Let us start by praying for God to give
success to the ministry we will undertake
in his name." Everyone saw this as the
way to start and the excitement settled.

In the calm each one prayed quietly.
Then Jesus said, "I hereby give you power
to preach God's good news, to heal the sick,
to help the poor, to tell those
who have lost hope that God is for them,
and to overcome evil with kindness,
wrong ideas with true ones.
Say everywhere: 'A community like heaven
where God rules is here. Come into it.'
Now, Judas, you have raised a helpful
question about money. I do not want you
to take money with you. The people to
whom you take the good news
will give you gifts. Dress simply.
Pray for the people you meet."
Then he nodded to James. "I will send
you out in six teams, two by two.
Peter," Jesus smiled, "you must be strong,
but not you only. For as there are those
who are coming out against me,
they will be against you, too.
You may be beaten, arrested, even put
in prison. Are you ready for that
possibility?" Jesus' serious mood spilled
over to his disciples. They were all feeling
very strong. They thought they were strong.
"And my Sons of Thunder," Jesus smiled,
"I want you to be as peaceful as doves.
If someone tries to pick a fight, pray
for him and leave. Do you understand?"
James and John nodded.
"And when the rulers or judges ask you
questions, trust God to help you answer
rightly. Answer as you think I would answer.

85

"And suppose you should be killed
on this trip because you follow me?
Do you trust me enough to die for me?"
They looked at one another.
They all thought they did.
"Do not be afraid of anything then,"
Jesus advised them.
"Remember, God is with you always.
Do not *your* special work. Do God's work."
Thaddaeus stood up. "Lord, tomorrow is the
day we have been preparing for. I am
filled with excitement."
"I can see you are, Thaddaeus,"
Jesus replied.
"God will do mighty works through you.
Remember that you are going in my place.
When someone welcomes you, it will be
just as if he were welcoming me."
Thaddaeus nodded that he understood.
"Since you give your life to serve God,
you will find now that you will really be
alive," Jesus said.
In the morning, the disciples two by two
went with uncertainty to their appointed
villages. But they met with such success
wherever they went that they knew God
was using them to increase his rule
in the lives of people. And they all were
glad in God's service and praised him often.

When the disciples met again with Jesus
as planned, they were full of their stories
of God's power among the people.
"In my presence, God healed many people

86

as I prayed for them," Matthew said, his
eyes full of excitement. "More people
than I could number promised
to follow your teachings, Master."
Said Simon the Zealot, "I even noticed
the number of soldiers who were anxious
to hear about God's kingdom of peace."
"Yes," Judas chimed in, "and we were
invited to eat and stay wherever we went.
Jesus," he announced, "we have received
many gifts for our work. Our treasury
is fuller now than before we went."
Jesus nodded but said nothing. He decided
to wait until the fish had finished cooking
over the campfire and all had eaten before
he would share his own news. After each had
told of his trip, its problems, but also
how God seemed always to be in the center
of their thoughts and deeds,
the twelve became quiet.
Jesus was looking over the lake.
This camping spot was his favorite.
"You have been very quiet through our
reports, Master," Bartholomew said.
"Is everything all right, Lord?"
The disciples turned to Jesus.
"Have our reports displeased you?
Did we not do as you wanted?"
Jesus turned to his friends.
"My friends! My friends! Your news
proves God is now upsetting the old ways
and blessing better ways of living.
God is always to be praised.
Do not forget to give God all the glory.

87

"Your words make me know that God keeps
every one of his promises. Even those who
aren't Jews by birth are believing
in God's kingdom and want to enter it, too.
This is a great day for the news you bring.
But it is a sad day for the news
I must share with you. For while
you report that God has blessed your efforts
with success, I know that even good efforts
sometimes are hurt by evil men
who seem to win for awhile."
The disciples grew tense. "What are you
trying to tell us?" they asked.
"My heart is sad to tell you that the
great man of God, God's own prophet, John
the Baptizer, has been murdered."
"Ohhhh!" the whole group groaned.
"King Herod has had his way. John is
dead!" Jesus said simply. "There is
danger in standing up for right against
the wrong. God may bless our work, but
he does not promise we will never be
harmed. He promises instead that we can
be brave standing firm by the right. And
if we must die serving God, what better
way is there? All men one day die.
He who dies for God will be of
great importance in God's
heavenly kingdom."

The news saddened everyone as it had Jesus.
But they became
all the more sure that God would use them
to spread his kingdom everywhere.

88

"Unless a seed die," Jesus said, remembering
his talk so long before with Brother David
by Beth-abara where he had heard the news
of John's arrest, "unless a seed die, how
can it become a healthy, growing plant?"
Everyone knew that the danger would be
greater now. "If Herod will kill so beloved
a prophet as John, where will he stop?"
they wondered. And they all stared at Jesus,
who was becoming far more famous
and more loved
than John ever had been.

The Camel Swallowers

Jesus continued to be welcomed in some
of the synagogues where he told the people
what God is like, what God expects
of his children, and what the people are
like when they accept God as their ruler.
"Do you mean we are important to God?"
many people asked. They seemed surprised.
"We have always thought God was far off
and wasn't at all interested in us."
"You are mistaken!" Jesus would say.
"In a country like ours, you know
how important our sheep are to us.
Well," Jesus said, "once there was
a good shepherd. He had one hundred
sheep. But one day, one strayed away
from him and was lost. Did he let it go
and say, 'What's the difference? I still
have ninety-nine left'? No, he did not!
He left his flock in charge of a helper
and went hunting everywhere until he found
that one little lamb that had wandered off!
And when he found it, he was happier just
then about that one sheep than he was
about the rest of the whole flock.
When he returned with his lost sheep,
he had a party for his friends
to celebrate his happiness.
God is no less interested in you than a
good shepherd is in each of his sheep."

90

"We have not realized God cares about us,"
people said.

"He does!" Jesus insisted. "God cares
for every one of you."

"Hold on, Jesus!" some people objected.
They were not happy about the
story. "You may be right that God cares
for everyone. But he loves some more than
others. Surely, God loves those who
keep his laws more than those who do not.
Surely," they argued, pulling themselves
up tall to show they felt themselves to be
better than some people, "God cares
more what happens to some of us than to
others. The fact that some of us are rich
shows that God loves us more."

91

Jesus shook his head. "You are wrong.
God does not play favorites. God is like
a good father. Does a good father play
favorites? Of course not! A good father
will deal with each child fairly and love
each one fully. Your riches do not mean
God loves a poor man less than you."
His teachings made some of the powerful
leaders of Galilee unhappy with Jesus.
"That Jesus is arousing the people!"
they said. "He leads the uneducated
and out-of-work people to believe that
God loves them as much as us."
"Yes," others joined in, "if Jesus keeps
talking like this, even those who never
step inside our synagogues will be
thinking themselves as good as
the religious leaders of our country."
Opposition to Jesus continued to grow
among some officials, too. So Jesus
preached more and more on the streets and
in the countryside. He became
less popular in some of the synagogues.
One day Peter overheard some talk against
Jesus. "Lord," Peter said, "I have heard
important people speak against you. I am
remembering that John the Baptist was
arrested and put to death for speaking so
bluntly to the leaders. I am worried about
you."
"I've heard such talk, too, Simon Peter,"
Jesus answered. "But can I tell lies just
because some do not like the truth? Only
when one tells the truth is God pleased."

92

But while some of the rich and highborn
people seemed to be unhappy with Jesus,
not everyone was. The poor people who
had never had a chance and the uneducated
people who could not afford to send their
children to school were very pleased.
Many were encouraged by Jesus' words.
"We thought we were unimportant. Now we
know we are really children of the King
of kings, the Lord God."

One day, Jesus suggested to his disciples
that they go into a nearby town to shop.
Many people gathered around Jesus.
Some religious leaders came up to him.
"We want to complain!" They looked angry.
"You claim your followers serve God.
But then you permit them to break
our religious laws. How come?"
James whispered to his brother, John.
"They look as if they're going
to start a fight."
John looked sternly at his brother.
"Son of Thunder, don't live up
to that nickname Jesus gave you.
Let Jesus handle this!"
"There are laws which are very important,"
Jesus smiled at the angry leaders.
"These are the laws God himself gives us.
You shall love God above everything.
That is one such law. Another is
that you should love each person as much as
you love yourself. Do you agree these are
God's laws?" Jesus wanted to know.

"Oh, yes!" they answered. "Since Moses
we have had those laws from God."
"But," Jesus went on, "there are other
rules which are not from God,
but which are only laws of men.
These laws may be all right to obey,
but some of them are not really important.
Some of these rules are even bad laws
and ought to be changed."
"On our last Sabbath rest day,
we saw you working instead of resting.
You broke the law," they charged.
James tightened his fists.
Jesus seemed surprised. "Tell me what
you saw, so I will know," he said.
"You were walking through a field with
several of your followers." They pointed to
James and John.
"As you walked, we saw you pull off the
heads of several stalks of wheat and
chew on them. That is working for it is
taking up a little harvest."
"Oh, really, now!" Jesus sighed.
"What a narrow-minded idea you have of

94

using the day God has set aside for your
rest and his worship. Did you know we
were actually talking about how to pray
best as we walked across that field?"
"Oh!" they said, pleased with themselves.
"What you *said* doesn't make any difference.
You broke a law. You worked on the rest
day. But we keep every law without
exception. That's a good example of how
you are leading the people away from God."
Jesus thought for a minute. Then he saw
some camels loping down the street.
"Which is more important in God's sight,"
Jesus asked them, "a camel or a man?"
They whispered together: "Why, a man
is more important than a camel,"
they finally answered.
"Then, why is it," Jesus wanted to know,
"that your laws say a man can pull his
camel out of a well if he falls into it
on our rest day, but if a man falls into
the same hole he must stay there
until the next day?"
The men looked at one another,
but they couldn't think of a good answer.
"You see," Jesus insisted, "that is an
example of man's law that is not really
God's law. God's law always puts a man
in first importance above an animal.
God wants us to obey his laws rather than
man-made rules when the two disagree,"
Jesus insisted. "If you gentlemen really
want to show God honor, you will obey
his laws above your own.

"Show love to all, show mercy, show respect
to the poor, forgive those who ask for it,
and treat every man as your brother.
But the leaders were not convinced.
They were even angrier because they
could not think of a good answer.
It seems to me," Jesus laughed, "you
are so busy trying to keep up with all
these tiny man-made rules, that you never
bother to live by the God-made rules."
The men turned red-faced with anger.
"He has made fools of us before this
crowd," they blushed.
The people in the market place
had come close to hear all this.
John looked at James. "Jesus got the best
of them," he whispered.
James winked at his brother.
Jesus' eyes twinkled. "In fact," he
said, "you are like the man with a big
strainer—so busy trying to keep a tiny
bug from getting into his mouth that he
never knew he swallowed a whole camel."
The thought of swallowing so big a beast
was funny to everyone except the men
who had been arguing with Jesus.
They pushed the crowd aside to leave.
"Make us look like fools will he?"
they sputtered as they left. They
knew they had lost the argument.
They were angry because they thought Jesus
had made fun of them. They missed
what Jesus had been trying to teach them.

96

A Crown or a Cross

"I don't like it! I don't like it at all,"
Simon the Zealot said to Thaddaeus.
He shook his head and looked around.
His eyes darted from place to place.
"Look at Jesus. He is not afraid.
His face is firm.
He must know he's in danger.
But there is no turning him back.
I've used every argument I can think of."
Thaddaeus rubbed his arm anxiously.
"Is there nothing we can do, Simon?"
Thaddaeus asked.
"Yes," Simon answered, "we must remember
that he is our leader and do as he says.
I try to remember that he has always
been right. He has never failed us."
Thaddaeus shook his head, agreeing.
"He is determined to go into Jerusalem.
But each year it has become less safe."
"It surely has," Simon the Zealot agreed.
"How quickly the days, the weeks,
the months have passed," Thaddaeus said.
"It seems so short a time since we agreed
to become Jesus' disciples.
These three years have passed quickly."
"Time does fly." Simon picked up
some pebbles as he spoke.
"We should know by now that Jesus wants
to celebrate the Passover in Jerusalem."

He threw the stones—one by one—
over the field.
Little clouds of dust rose as they hit the
dry soil. He added, "And let us hope
Herod will not make this our last visit
to Jerusalem! Perhaps Jesus will let the
people declare him to be their king
as Herod fears."
"The people say: 'Jesus, our King. Jesus,
King of the Jews!' Often we are hearing
these cries," Thaddaeus remembered.
"Many people want Jesus to take over the
government. I think he has more support
from the people than any leader since
the days of King David himself."
Judas came toward them.
"Have you heard?" he asked, brushing away
some flies that were circling his face.
"Heard what?" The two men turned to look
straight into Judas' face.
"We are going into the city tomorrow."
Judas motioned down the road.
"The city will be crowded with all these
travelers going there, too."
"Well, that's no surprise, Judas,"
Thaddaeus chuckled. "Why have we come
so far if not to go into the city?"
He shook his head. "I had hoped you were
going to tell us you had convinced
Jesus to turn back.
Why walk straight into their stronghold?
His enemies are strongest in Jerusalem."
But Simon was not in a mood to tease Judas.
"Be serious, Thaddaeus," he spoke out.

98

"Judas," his voice grew excited,
"did Jesus agree? Is he going to let
you rent some great white horses so that
we can enter the city in a parade?"
Before Judas could answer, other disciples
were gathering around to listen.
"That would be great!" Simon said. "I
can imagine Jesus on a great white charger,
the twelve of us following him on handsome
prancing horses with thousands
upon thousands of pilgrims marching behind.
And cheering crowds would line the streets
to see our parade. Herod wouldn't dare
touch us then for fear of the people.
Let everyone know we're there.
That's my idea. If the people of Jerusalem
don't know we are there, one of Herod's
spies will surely find it out. Then we
could be arrested without the people being
able to protest."
Bartholomew smiled and poked Simon in

99

the ribs with a playful jab: "Arrest Jesus,
perhaps, but why you, Simon?
Do you think Herod is worrying
about you?" Simon blushed.
"Steady, Simon," Judas interrupted.
"Jesus is not one to want any parades to
show his popularity. In fact, he has
asked Matthew and me to go into town to
get a young colt for him to ride
tomorrow. It's not a white charger,
but instead it is a lowly colt no soldier
would want to be seen riding."
Judas shook his head. "Imagine that sight.
God's King on a poor man's transportation
and all of us straggling behind on foot."
Simon the Zealot motioned to the others
to come close. "If he would but say a
word," Simon nodded, "Jesus could summon
a great army of angels to protect him.
If he is from God, surely God will not let
harm come to him. What army can stand
against God?"
Thaddaeus spoke up. "Jesus has never used
his power for himself. For others,
yes, but not for himself."
"Well," said Simon, "if Jesus is to be
God's King, Jerusalem might be the place
for him to be hailed King, and this very
week the time. Jesus would make a new
kind of King—really out to help the people.
But in any case, I'm prepared to protect us."
Simon opened his travel robe to show
a sword hanging from his hip.
The other disciples gasped in surprise.

100

"Is it going to be that bad?"
Bartholomew's brow was raised.
"Oh, you won't have to use that, Simon,"
Judas chimed in. "Surely, at the first
sign of trouble, God will protect his Son
and us. If enemies should try to take him,
wow! God's full power will be displayed.
Lightning! Thunder! Earthquakes!
God's power is endless. I am sure of it."
"No matter!" the Zealot whispered—hitting
his sword, covered again by his cloak.
"I am prepared. It is no harm to be ready
to defend yourself. And Peter carries a
sword, too. At least two of us
will be ready."
Thaddaeus shook his head. "You had better
not let Jesus see you with that. Remember
his words: 'If you live by the sword, you
can expect to be killed by a sword.'"
"Oh really, Thaddaeus!" Simon said with
his hands on his hips. "Since when has
carrying a sword for an emergency been
'living by the sword'?"
Judas said to the Zealot, "I agree with
you, Simon. Jesus is not worried about
going to Jerusalem. I really think he is
going to tell the people this week that
he has come to be their King. And the
people will welcome him.
James and John think so too.
But what do you think of their asking for
the most important jobs when Jesus becomes
King? What nerve! They want to be ahead
of all the rest of us in his kingdom."

Thaddaeus spoke again. "But Jesus said
they didn't know what they were asking for.
He told them that instead of wanting the
most important jobs, they should seek to
be the most helpful in serving others.
In God's kingdom, people who serve the
most are the most important."
"Well, I may be wrong," Judas said, "but
I believe Jesus will be King before long.
With his power from God, no one will stop
him. And if James and John want to be
Jesus' first assistants, I might expect
to be the treasurer of the new state."
"I don't think you have understood Jesus."
Thaddaeus shook his head, looking first
at Judas and then to Simon the Zealot.
"Jesus has told us that he is not to be
a king like King Herod."
Said Simon, defending himself, "But how
will his enemies know he is God's King
if he does not take a king's crown?
It doesn't seem right for God's great Son
to ride on a lowly colt, leading a parade
into Jerusalem with all of us
following behind on foot!"
Judas, agreeing, shook his head. "It's not
what I had pictured for tomorrow."
Matthew, who had been silent,
now spoke up.
"Yes," he said, "Jesus is God's King. But
I do not think Jesus wants Herod's crown.
Our King needs no such crown."
Judas looked back as he picked up his
walking stick and said, "I think you're

102

wrong, Matthew. I think you're wrong.
If Jesus doesn't choose to be King in
Jerusalem, he can expect trouble from
King Herod. King Herod might have him
arrested. King Herod might even have
him killed . . . on a cross!"
The disciples' hearts thumped faster.
Matthew shivered at the idea of a cross.

To See for Himself

How sad they were!
Peter, Andrew, James, and John
could find nothing to laugh about.
Peter shook his head slowly.
"None of us understood all he told us,"
he said almost as if he were talking
to himself. "But to have failed him
in his time of greatest danger, that
is unforgivable!"
Peter struggled to keep from crying.
"Now, Peter," his longtime friend, John,
comforted him. "Jesus himself always said
God is quick to forgive. And you well
know Jesus would have been the first
to forgive you if he were here."
"I know! I know!" Peter sputtered.
"But three times I said I had never met Jesus.
What a lie! And just to keep from being
arrested. The least I could have done
was to say proudly that I was his follower."
"None of us did well by Jesus that night,"
James added. "Peter, every one of the twelve
of us failed Jesus after his arrest."
Andrew stood up to put his arm around his
brother. "Come now, Peter. Remember it
was you whom Jesus named 'the rock.'
This is a time for acting strong like
your name. What you did by saying you did
not know Jesus was not as bad as what

104

Judas did." At the mention of Judas' name,
Andrew felt Peter's broad shoulders shiver.
James picked up the thought. "Why did
he do it? Why?" He was thinking about
Judas. They all were. "Why did he lead
the soldiers right to Jesus? Why did he
have to kiss Jesus? What a terrible use
for a kiss!" James' voice trembled.
"A kiss to make sure the enemies knew
the Master from us. What a way to betray
a friend. What a traitor!" Peter sobbed.
"I wish I hadn't carried that sword.
When I drew it to defend him, Jesus'
touch and look said I had failed him."

105

"We were all wrong," said James. "I think
Judas really thought Jesus would use his
power from God to call on the angels, to
raise an army, and to become a King. Judas
was wrong, but none of us understood
Jesus." James moved his chair a little.
"My heart trembled when we were in the
upper room before the arrest."
John answered, "So did mine. I knew
I had really misunderstood Jesus then.
James and I had asked for the best jobs
when Jesus became the King.
But when Jesus took the water bowl and
the towel to kneel before each of us and
wash our feet, I could have died of shame!
Imagine, the one we honored as from God
humbling himself to wash our dusty feet."
Peter hit his leg with his fist. "And I
said, 'You will never wash my feet, Lord.'
And Jesus said, 'If I do not wash your feet,
you can never understand what I want you
to be!' And I had to say, 'Then help me
to get clean thoughts and a pure heart too!' "
Everyone was silent a long time.
Then Peter straightened up. "I think we
were all misled by Jesus' popularity when
we entered Jerusalem. What crowds there
were! What cheering and waving of
palm branches. And what singing, too!
Jesus got a king's welcome even though
he was riding on that little colt."
Andrew's eyes brightened. "That was really
a great parade, wasn't it?" he said as he
remembered. "I was embarrassed at first,
but even there Jesus was trying to show

106

what God's kingdom is like. It is not a
kingdom of soldiers and harsh rulers making
people jump to obey. Rather, God brings
kindliness and peace and the helpfulness
that makes for peace. Jesus' love was
complete. He loved the people, all the
people. He did not seek to rule them,
but to lead them. He did not want us
to follow him because we were afraid of
him, but because we loved him."
Peter's face brightened with a small smile.
"It's true," he agreed. "He was all love.
All of us loved him because he first
loved us." Peter lingered on that thought.
"But he is dead now. Dead! Dead!"
The words echoed around the room.
"Even goodness and love like we saw in Jesus
cannot cut through hate and evil. His
enemies have won. God did not stop them.
Jesus would not let us stop them.
Now he lies in a borrowed tomb.
When he asked us to pray with
him, we fell asleep in the garden."
"During his trial, Jesus was alone. All
of us had run away to hide," Andrew said.
"Not one of us stayed to say a good word
for him." Andrew winced,
"It is hard to think of him being beaten.
And convicted on lies! And made to carry
that huge wooden cross up the hill."
Peter stared blankly at the wall. He said:
"They nailed him to a cross! To a cross!"
James spoke to Andrew,

"When I close my eyes I can see
Jesus praying for the very men
who put him there, 'Father, forgive
them. They don't understand.'"
Peter looked up. "He was praying that
for me, too."
John shook his head. "He could have
prayed it for all of us."
James moved his chair. They all
were tired, but no one could sleep.
James said: "The sign above him . . . yes.
Do you remember? This is 'Jesus, King
of the Jews!'" Peter stood to walk
around the room. "The sign was right.
Jesus is the King. He was
the King of forgiveness and love if I
ever saw it. That King is one everyone
needs. Surely, God will not let such a life
end like that. Perhaps our dream did not
die on the cross.
Perhaps, perhaps," Peter hesitated as
a big idea took words in his mind.
"Perhaps Jesus had to die for God, for us.
Maybe," he went on, "maybe he was trying
to prepare us for this all the time.
Remember he said we had to be ready to
take up a cross to follow him."
"What are you trying to say, Peter?"
Andrew asked, looking puzzled.
Peter answered, "I'm thinking of all the
times Jesus told us God expects us to love
and serve him above everything else.
Remember what he said?
'Do not fear death. Just love God.'"
"Yes. Yes," the other three answered.

108

Peter continued: "Jesus not only told us
what God is like.
He showed us. He told us to love those
who hate us. He loved his enemies from
a cross. He told us to believe. His
last words were of trust in God. He told
us that in order to live for God, we should
not be afraid to die. And he said that in
dying, we will be raised up by God to a
new life that will never end."
Peter went to the corner to pick up his
cloak. "Come on!" he shouted. "What
are we hiding here for? Whose followers
are we? Let us go to find the others.
God has not let Jesus die altogether.
Something of the Christ is now alive in me."

The sun was climbing in the sky as
the men went to friends' houses in Jerusalem
looking for the possible hiding places of
the other disciples. As they turned the
corner in the morning cool, they heard the
voices of women excitedly calling.
The little company of men paused to look
at three women racing toward them.
The women were panting so hard they could
hardly speak. "We have been to the tomb,"
one said, panting.
"It is another miracle of God,"
said the second.
"God be praised!" shouted the third.
The men looked at one another,
not knowing what to think.

109

"What is it? What is it?" Peter demanded.
"It is Jesus. We have seen him," said one.
"God has returned his life to him
and we have seen him," said a second.
"We have talked with him," said the third.
Peter looked from one to the other.
"He is alive?" Peter asked, not daring
to believe such good news. "He is alive?
How is that possible?"
"What is not possible with God?" the
first woman responded.
"Hallelujah!" The other two sang and
jumped up and down for joy.
Almost not daring to believe, but bursting
with joy, the little group embraced with
hugs and shouts of joy.
"Thanks be to God. His Son lives again.
Hallelujah!" Andrew's arms were waving.
"Oh, what little trust in God we have
had," Peter said. "The Christ
is alive. God gave him this victory.
Jesus the Christ is King of kings!"
It took only a minute to decide. The rest
of the disciples must be told of all God
had done. The women went in one direction.
Andrew, James, and John went in another.
But Peter, believing such news almost too
good to be true, set out at a fast run
to find the tomb where Jesus' body had
been laid, to see for himself!

As the four New Testament Gospels are interpretations of the life of Jesus, so *To Find Jesus* is a witness of faith in him. It is not desirable that this fictionalized account of our Lord's life should take the place of the Bible record. It is hoped the actual Bible text will be more meaningful because of the reading of this story.